Jo Boyd

ACTIVATE THE HEALER WITHIN

The Ultimate Tapping Handbook for Beginners

ACTIVATE
THE HEALER WITHIN

The Ultimate Tapping Handbook for Beginners

by Jo Boyd

2nd Edition

Author: Jo Boyd

Cover design, illustration: Jana Keller

American English – Original Edition

Receive your **free** '*Tapping Point Chart*' and '*7-Day Tapping Journal*' to keep track of your improvements by sending us an email with the subject **Tapping Journal** here: **benefit@healworld.ch**

CONTENTS

CHAPTER 1

Meridian Tapping: A gateway to self-healing

What is Tapping?

The premise is simple: our bodies are made up of energy pathways called meridians. When these pathways are blocked or out of balance, we experience physical or emotional discomfort. *Meridian Tapping* involves gentle tapping on specific points along these meridians while focusing on negative emotions or issues, helping you release blockages, and restore balance.

Much like tuning a musical instrument for the perfect harmony, our bodies also need fine-tuning to function at their optimal best. This tuning is achieved through **Meridian Tapping** a technique also known as *Thought Field Therapy* (TFT), *Emotional Freedom Techniques* (EFT), or *Meridian Energy Technique* (MET).

The essence of *Meridian Tapping* is not about creating something new within you; it's about transforming what already exists. It's about activating your inherent energy for self-healing.

The foundation of *Meridian Tapping* was laid by Traditional Chinese Medicine (TCM), over 2000 years ago through the discovery and definition of the Meridians.

In *Traditional Chinese Medicine,* acupuncture is used to correct usually physical disorders, by placing needles onto certain points along meridians. Meridians are defined as energetic pathways that run through your body. These pathways are measurable channels that act as highways for energy – called Qi, and are the base of many health practices in Asian culture. According to traditional Chinese medicine, **positive emotions indicate a free flow of energy, while negative emotions indicate a** blocked flow of energy.

With *Meridian Tapping* these pathways are tapped instead of needled. And not just to eliminate physical problems, but above all to reduce anxiety, help with phobias, and change negative emotions or patterns of belief, before they turn into physical symptoms.

Simply explained, tapping can be thought of as acupuncture with fingers.

The simplicity and user-friendly nature of *Meridian Tapping,* makes it accessible to anyone and anywhere, regardless of their prior experience with alternative medicine or other healing practices. No special equipment or extensive training is required, making it a versatile tool for self-healing.

The Evolution of Meridian Tapping: TFT, EFT, and MET

The rise of *Meridian Tapping Techniques,* such as Thought Field Therapy (TFT) and Emotional Freedom Techniques (EFT), have marked over the past 40 years, a significant evolution in the field of alternative healing and self-help practices, today also referred to as Meridian Energy Technique (MET).

The science of *Meridian Tapping* began not with a research grant, but rather with a woman suffering from an irrational fear of water.

Dr. Callahan, a psychologist, had treated Mary's aquaphobia for 18 months with a variety of psychotherapeutic methods, without alleviating the problem.

He knew about meridians and how they may affect our health. Spontaneously, he began to tap just under Maria's eye which is the end point of the stomach meridian. This was because she had mentioned an upset stomach in connection to her fear of water and he felt it could be helpful.

To everybody's surprise, the tapping removed every trace of Mary's phobic fear and her nightmares centering around this problem.

Through this experience, Dr. Callahan pioneered Thought Field Therapy (TFT) in the 1980s, establishing the foundational principles of tapping on meridian points to alleviate psychological distress.

Gary Craig, inspired by Callahan's work, simplified TFT into what became known as Emotional Freedom Techniques (EFT) in the 1990s. While both shared the belief in tapping techniques' efficacy, they diverged in approach. Callahan's TFT involved complex algorithms and specific sequences for different issues, while Craig sought to make the technique more accessible and universal by creating a simplified, adaptable tapping sequence: *The 9-Point Sequence*. Despite differences in methodology, their collective efforts significantly contributed to the widespread recognition and use of tapping therapies, demonstrating the transformative potential of addressing emotional and psychological issues through tapping on meridian points.

EFT has proven that tapping only 9 of 365 of the recognized acupuncture points on the meridians is enough to receive lasting results.

The Meridian Energy Technique (MET), however, has taught us that only 6 of the 9 tapping points, and in particular the collarbone point, are the most effective for dissolving negative emotions. **The collarbone point can even be used on its own for dissolving negative emotions.** This makes MET the most simplified yet effective version of all tapping techniques.

In this book you will be introduced to both techniques, the 9-point sequence, and the 6-point sequence along with a step-by-step manual to find out for yourself which suits you best and especially, which gives you the best results.

Understanding the Science

Since its inception, *Meridian Tapping* has gained popularity worldwide. It is used by therapists, counselors, and people in over 20 countries, including the United States, Canada, Australia, the United Kingdom, and Germany. Despite the ongoing debate about its effectiveness, the global reach of *Meridian Tapping* is a testament to its appeal and potential benefits.

"When I observe a number of suffering patients who did not respond to our usual treatment modalities, suddenly get better after TFT algorithms are given, I don't need a double-blind controlled study to tell me the value of TFT."
James McKoy, MD Chief, Pain Clinic, Chief Rheumatology Services Assistant Chief, Neuroscience Department, Hawaii

Tapping might be an easy-to-implement technique, but it is grounded in scientific principles.
The existence of the meridians has been scientifically proven using various Methods, e.g. with the aid of a radioactive tracer substance by French scientists as early as 1985 and using an infrared technique in 2005, by Prof. Dr. Popp and Dr. Schlebusch.

Research has shown that stimulating acupressure points can lead to a reduction in cortisol, the stress hormone, and an increase in the production of endorphins, the body's natural feel-good chemicals.

This has the effect of reducing stress, anxiety, and even physical pain.

According to a 2012 study by pioneering researcher and clinical psychologist Dr. Peta Stapleton, a single hour of tapping can change **72 genes** and reduce the stress hormone cortisol by **24 percent!** By comparison, napping reduces cortisol by only 14 percent.

A replicated study in 2020, again led by Dr. Peta Stapleton, added a twist: when participants tapped not only with a practitioner but also with a group, they got a **43 percent** reduction in cortisol.

Moreover, when you tap while focusing on a specific emotional or physical issue, you're engaging the brain's amygdala, which is responsible for processing emotions. This dual activation—tapping on acupressure points and addressing emotional issues—creates a profound effect on the brain, effectively rewiring and releasing emotional blockages, with one of the examples being Whoopi Goldberg's fear of flying:

Aviophobia is an anxiety disorder that afflicts about 25 million Americans and one of them was Academy Award-winning actress Whoopi Goldberg.

Whoopi's fear had a very real source. In 1978, she was living in San Diego and was on the balcony of her apartment with her then-4-year-old. It was then that Whoopi witnessed the PSA Flight 182 midair collision with a Cessna that claimed the lives of 135 people.

When the musical *Sister act,* based on Whoopi's smash-hit comedy from the 90s, opened in London's West End in 2009, the producers wanted Whoopi to be present. But the thought alone made her sweat; she was afraid that she would have a panic attack, but couldn't refuse the offer: *"The man that I'm working for sent his plane. (...) The thinking was, 'If I do freak out, nobody knows. No one writes about it."*

The Actress was treated by Virgin Atlantic's *Fear Of Flying* program and Dr. Roger Callahan's TFT Tapping Therapy.

Sitting in an airplane after a decade without air travel, Whoopi admitted that she was still uncomfortable throughout the flight, and had a few white-knuckle moments, but she landed safely in London without incident - a terrific victory for an aviophobe.

Her fear of flying and treatment were discussed on the television show *The View (2009).*

History and Origins in a Nutshell

100 BCE: The earliest documented reports of acupuncture

Acupuncture's origins can be traced back to ancient China, where it emerged as a fundamental component of traditional Chinese medicine (TCM). The earliest documented records of acupuncture date back to around 100 BCE during the Han Dynasty, compiled in the foundational text of Chinese medicine, *the Huangdi Neijing* (Yellow Emperor's Inner Canon), between 300 BCE and 100 CE, including theories and principles that form the basis of acupuncture.

6th and 7th Century AD: Spread and Influence

Acupuncture spread throughout East Asia and became an integral part of medical practices in countries like Korea and Japan. Each region developed its variations and interpretations of acupuncture.

The practice of acupuncture encountered challenges during periods of political and cultural change in China, including when it was suppressed or faced skepticism from mainstream medicine. However, it persisted due to its efficacy and cultural significance.

1950s: Modernization and Global Recognition

Acupuncture gained attention in the Western world during the latter half of the 20th century. Its effectiveness in pain management and various health conditions garnered interest among Western practitioners and researchers, leading to studies exploring its mechanisms and efficacy.

1980s: Emergence of Thought Field Therapy (TFT)

The roots of meridian tapping can be traced back to the 1980s when psychologist Roger Callahan developed *Thought Field Therapy,* combining principles from various fields; including traditional Chinese medicine, psychology, and applied kinesiology, to create a Method to alleviate emotional distress, such as anxiety, phobias, trauma, and more. Callahan's work introduced the concept of tapping on specific meridian points in a particular sequence to address various psychological issues. TFT was initially structured with complex algorithms for different problems and was used primarily in clinical settings.

1990s: Evolution into Emotional Freedom Techniques (EFT)

Gary Craig, a former student of Callahan, inspired by TFT, simplified and expanded upon Callahan's work, leading to the emergence of *Emotional Freedom Techniques* in the 1990s. Craig aimed to create a more user-friendly and accessible method that could be applied broadly to various emotional and physical issues. EFT simplified the tapping process by utilizing a 9-point sequence while focusing on specific problems or issues.

2000s: Further development into Meridian Energy Technique (MET), Popularization and Recognition
Throughout the 2000s, the popularity of meridian tapping techniques grew significantly and gained recognition among practitioners and the public as a self-help tool for managing stress, anxiety, phobias, trauma, and various emotional and psychological concerns. This decade saw the emergence of workshops, training programs, and online resources that contributed to the spread and accessibility of these techniques.

One of them made a difference; When Rainer and Regina Franke, a German therapist couple (a qualified psychologist and an alternative practitioner and classical homeopath) tested the tapping with doubt, they were quickly proven wrong. Like all other therapists in the field, they were used to working with clients over a long period, sometimes for years, without any significant improvement. With tapping the success rate could even be counted in hours. Instead of seeing this as a threat to their professions, they started teaching and educating people in an even more simplified tapping technique called *Meridian Energy Technique* (MET).

2010s: Research and Integration

The 2010s marked a period where meridian tapping began to attract attention from researchers and clinicians interested in its potential therapeutic effects. While more traditional fields initially viewed these techniques with skepticism, scientific studies started to explore their efficacy. Research focused on areas such as stress reduction, emotional regulation, pain management, and the physiological effects of tapping on the body's stress response.

2020s: Continued Growth and Diversification

In recent years, meridian tapping has continued to evolve around the globe. The techniques have expanded beyond their initial psychological focus to encompass physical well-being, personal development, and performance enhancement. Due to the effectiveness of tapping, a variety of professionals integrate it today into their practices, and due to the techniques' simplicity, it found a broad use for successful self-application.

CHAPTER 2

The Mind-Body Connection:

Understanding Our Emotions as Premonition to Physical Illness

Emotions are more than just feelings; they can significantly influence our physical health. The US scientist Candace B. Pert, an accomplished neuroscientist and pharmacologist once stated that 'Your body is your subconscious mind.'

"Most psychologists treat the mind as disembodied, a phenomenon with little or no connection to the physical body. Conversely, physicians treat the body with no regard for the mind or the emotions. But the body and mind are not separate, and we cannot treat one without the other." Dr. Candace Pert

Pert has proven that emotions are converted into the body's chemical signals in the brain (neuropeptides) in the hypothalamus and reach the receptors of the cells via the bloodstream. There they trigger corresponding body reactions. This is why we turn red with shame, get 'butterflies' in our stomachs or have diarrhea from excitement. Pert refers to the connecting pathways between the body and mind as 'information channels'.

She further explained that "Our physical body can be changed by the emotions we experience." This means that our thoughts and emotions can directly impact our physical health.

Negative thoughts or unresolved emotional issues can manifest as physical symptoms over time. For instance, anxiety can cause stomachaches; prolonged stress may lead to high blood pressure or heart disease; even back pain could be linked to suppressed anger or resentment.

When our bodies show signs of illness, we often turn to conventional medicine for answers to treat the physical symptoms only. This is like shutting the stable doors after the horse has bolted – you may or may not catch the horse. While it still is essential to consult with a medical professional, addressing these underlying emotional issues is crucial for holistic well-being – something that is often overlooked.

This is great news: It means by addressing our emotions before they turn into symptoms, we can affect the outcome and with a little bit of practice gain control over our well-being!

Emotions Are the Key

Emotions are our body's way of communicating with us. We can either shut them off because they may be annoying, uncomfortable, or confusing or we can learn to listen and act upon them. This is where *Meridian Tapping* steps in —it acts like an interpreter between you and your body's language.

Let's consider migraines—a common ailment suffered by many worldwide. A study published in the *Cephalalgia Journal* found a strong correlation between emotional stress and the severity of migraines.

Now imagine using *Meridian Tapping* techniques during heightened states of distress—in essence, 'tapping' away at those invisible blockages of emotional turmoil before they solidify into throbbing headaches. In this case, you are not just addressing the symptom, but also decoding and resolving the emotional undercurrent causing it.
Meridian Tapping can help you decode your body's language of emotions, allowing you to address the root cause of physical symptoms.

Think of your body as a grand mansion. Each room represents different bodily functions—with the electricity lines running throughout it all, representing the pathways of your life energy, called meridians. They light up every room if the connection is ensured.

Through tapping specific points on your meridians, you can release trapped negative emotions that contribute to your physical discomforts. There is no need to dive further into the discomfort of these emotions nor to live through painful memories. All you must do is **feel** the emotion you would like to dissolve with tapping.

Avoid making the common mistake of dismissing this powerful connection between our bodies and our minds. Our emotions are part of an incredible communication system, like smoke detectors warning to prevent a potential fire. All we have to do is take notice when emotions emerge, define what we feel, and start dissolving the energy block through tapping before they manifest in our bodies influencing their functions profoundly.

A psychoneuroimmunology study found that chronic emotional stress is significantly associated with the risk of developing physical illnesses, including heart disease and cancer. The researchers found that stress can alter the immune system's function, making the body more susceptible to disease. This means that managing our emotions and stress levels could potentially reduce our risk of illness.

Full citation: Kiecolt-Glaser, J. K., McGuire, L., Robles, T. F., & Glaser, R. (2002). Emotions, morbidity, and mortality: new perspectives from psychoneuroimmunology. Annual review of psychology, 53(1), 83-107.

Learning to read and address these signals with *Meridian Tapping* is like getting a master key for your grand mansion—now, you can keep every room illuminated.

Key Takeaways

- Our emotions significantly impact our physical health.
- Physical ailments often have an underlying emotional component that needs addressing for complete healing.
- *Meridian Tapping* can be used effectively to decode the language of our bodies and release trapped negative emotions contributing to physical discomforts.
- Always seek professional advice for persistent or severe symptoms.

CHAPTER 3

A Step-by-Step Guide to Meridian Tapping (1/2)

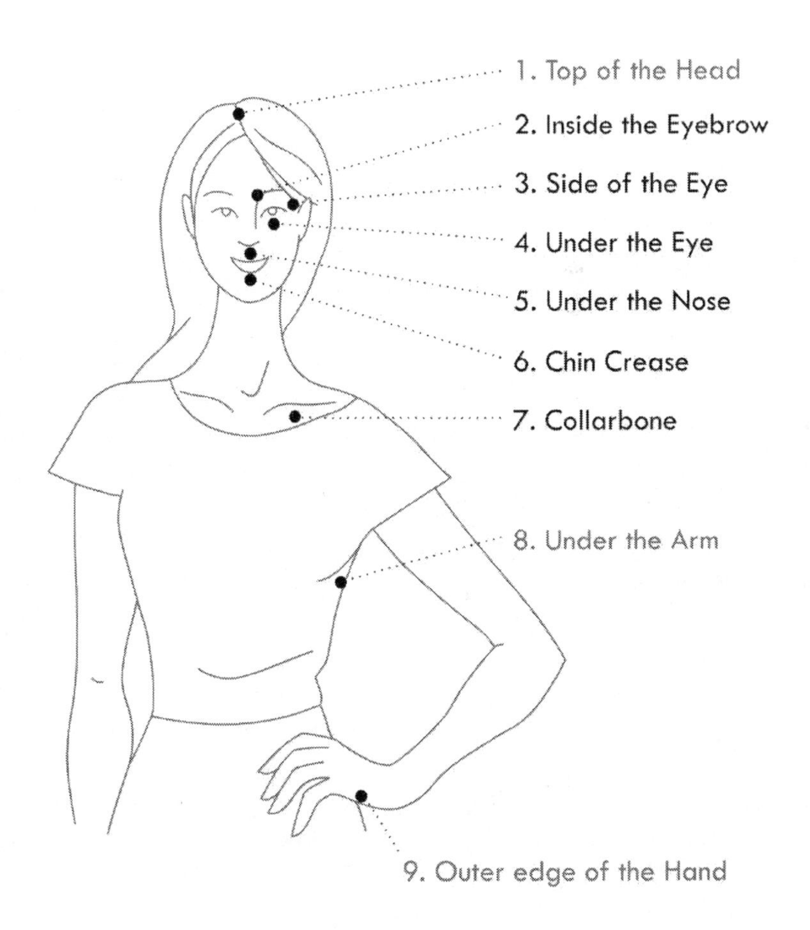

Where to tap?

Tapping focuses on following illustrated acupressure points, also known as meridian points, located on the body's energy pathways. The meridians that have been selected are the basic primary channels with their endpoints close to the skin, making them the most easily accessible.

Depending on the sequence, 6 to 9 meridian points in the picture are tapped. The picture gives you a visual template for the points, to get a feeling for them.

The primary tapping points include:

1. **Top of Head Point:**
Found at the crown of the head. This is often used as the setup point for your tapping sequence.

2. **Inside the Eyebrow Point:**
Situated at the beginning of either eyebrow, just above the bridge of the nose.

3. **Side of Eye Point:**
Found on the bone at the outside corner of either eye.

4. Under Eye Point:
Located just below the center of either eye, on the bone.

5. Under Nose Point:
Positioned in the area between the nose and the upper lip.

6. Chin Point:
Situated in the small crease between the chin and the lower lip.

7. Collarbone Point:
Located in the hollow just below the collarbone and slightly to the side, on both sides of the chest.

8. Under Arm Point:
Positioned approximately a hand width below the armpit, on the side of your ribs.

9. Karate Chop Point:
Located on the outer edge of your hand, just below the little finger. This also may be used as the setup point for your tapping sequence.

How to tap?

Tapping is very simple; All you need to do is tap your fingers on this specific group of meridian points one after another and repeat.

The points only need to be tapped approximately; it's not about working to the millimeter. Tap gently with 2-3 fingers on the corresponding points, it should feel noticeable and pleasant. Points shown on the right side of the body in the diagram can be tapped on the left side with the same results. You are also welcome to switch sides while tapping.

You can tap with either hand, using the tips of your index and middle finger(s). Each point should be tapped around ten times without intention <u>or</u> as long as you repeat your intention at each point.

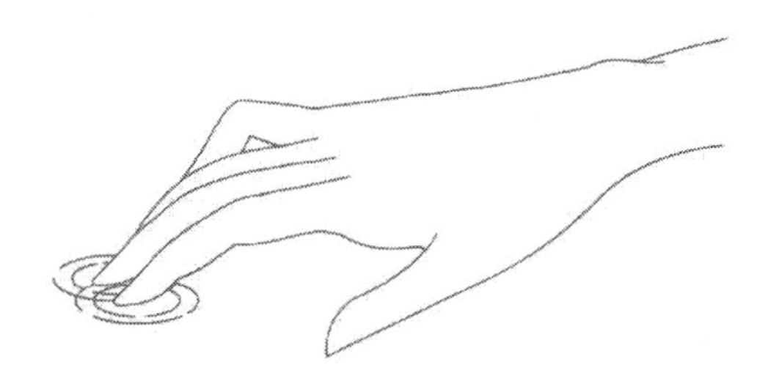

What to tap?

Everything that burdens you emotionally.

But let's start at the beginning. Like gardening, the preparations start long before you plant the seeds. It needs a hospitable environment for plants to grow. This means **preparing the soil** – removing stones, pulling weeds, mulching...

The same is true with tapping. We all go straight to planting and then wonder why our flowers and fruit trees quickly wither.

I am happy! I am healthy! I am successful!

These affirmations might feel good for a moment, but they often don't stick because the soil doesn't support their growth yet.

When we start tapping on our outcome, without preparing the soil, we set ourselves up for frustration. On the other hand, when we start tapping to prepare the soil, something beautiful – and lasting – starts to sprout.

That's why we start with the weeds like gardeners: the unpleasant thoughts in your head and uncomfortable sensations in your body.

CHAPTER 3

A step-by Step Guide to Meridian Tapping (2/2)

The 9-point sequence

Now you might be standing in your overgrown garden wide-eyed and overwhelmed, without knowing where to possibly start.
This is why we simply ease into the first round without speaking or intention. Just relax and observe: Is there a negative emotion showing up?

To make this easy, we start with a guided tapping sequence, going through all four rounds as listed below. Each of them with different intentions and statements.

Round 1:
Tapping without speaking or intention
Round 2:
Defining the negative emotion and allowing it to be there
Round 3:
Neutralizing the emotion
Round 4:
Transforming the emotion into something positive

Let's start together with round 1...!

Round 1: Tapping without speaking or intention

Start by tapping the outer edge of your hand, (app. 10x right or left) and continue to the next tapping point until you finish with the point under your arm.

1. **The outer edge of your hand**
2. **The top of your head**
3. **The inside of your eyebrows**
4. **The side of your eyes**
5. **Under the eyes**
6. **Under the nose**
7. **Under your mouth above the chin**
8. **Under your collarbone**
9. **Under your arm**

If an emotion surfaced during your first tapping round, note it down and rate it on a scale of 1 to 10 (1 = non-existent / 10 = incredibly strong) and proceed to round 2.

____

1 2 3 4 5 6 7 8 9 10

Round 2: Defining the negative emotion and allowing it to be there

In the second round, it's time to pick a weed and create tapping statements. You continue either with the negative emotion that surfaced in round 1 or you define the issue that you want to work on with the help of *Meridian Tapping*. Be as specific and brief as possible in your formulation. If you wish to define an emotion to work on, feel inside yourself:

What negative emotion do you feel in this moment (e.g. fear, anger, sadness)? Where in your body do you feel this emotion (e.g. solar plexus/ belly/ chest/ head)?

Rate the emotion on a scale of 1 to 10 (1 = non-existent / 10 = incredibly strong). Where are you on this scale right now?

Emotion:______________________________________

Location:______________________________________

1 2 3 4 5 6 7 8 9 10

1. The outer edge of your hand

In this second step, start again by tapping the outer edge of your hand (right or left) and pick or add the emotion appropriate to you.

"Even if I feel [afraid, angry, sad…] I love and accept myself as I am."

Now feel into yourself at the next acupressure points and connect with the [fear/anger/sadness/...] Feel the negative emotion, notice where it is in your body, and let it be there.

Continue tapping on the outer edge of your hand and describe the negative emotion in more detail:

"Even when I am [afraid/ angry/ sad/ ...], I love and accept myself as I am."
"Even if I am incredibly [afraid/ angry/ sad/ ...], I love and accept myself as I am."
"Even though I have known this [fear/ anger/ sadness/ ...] for so long, I love and accept myself as I am."

2. Top of your head
"I have known this emotion for so long."
"I have known this fear/anger/ sadness for so long."

3. Inside of your eyebrows
"I can feel it in my [solar plexus/ belly/ chest/ head…]."

4. Side of the eyes
"This [fear/ anger/ sadness/...], has been with me for so long and I feel like I have to fight so hard to be seen and loved."

5. Under the eyes
"This fighting is so exhausting. I'm so tired of fighting."
"I am so tired of being [afraid/ angry/ sad/ ...]."
"This [fear/ anger/ sadness/ ...] is so exhausting."

6. Under the nose
"But I've known it for so long and I don't even know who I am without this [fear/ anger/ sadness/ ...]. That's okay."

7. Under your mouth above the chin
"This [fear/ anger/ sadness/ ...], somehow it belongs to me. My body knows this [fear/ anger/ sadness/ ...] so well."
"This [fear/ anger/ sadness/ ...] comes so much faster than love and I'm so used to it."

8. Under your collarbone

"It's okay that the [fear/ anger/ sadness/ ...] is there."
"If I'm honest, it has helped me many times."
"It has helped me to stop being hurt."
"But when I feel into my heart, I think that's not true at all."

9. Under your arm

"This [fear/ anger/ sadness/ ...], it's okay that it's there. I stop fighting this [fear/ anger/ sadness/ ...]."

Take a deep breath and rate the emotion again on a scale of 1 to 10. How intense is it for you now?

Emotion:____________ Location:_____________

Scale: 1 2 3 4 5 6 7 8 9 10

Emotion:____________ Location:_____________

Scale: 1 2 3 4 5 6 7 8 9 10

Emotion:____________ Location:_____________

Scale: 1 2 3 4 5 6 7 8 9 10

Round 3: Neutralizing the Emotion

Now it is time to create a hospitable environment for our future flowers and fruit trees.

If you notice an initial relaxation, you can now adopt a neutral level. Imagine that you are making a peace offering to your emotions.

Now say sentences that express an accepting attitude towards the emotion and tap the 9 acupressure points again:

1. Outer edge of your hand
"Even when there is [fear/ anger/ sadness/ ...], I love and accept myself as I am."
"Even though these emotions are there, I love and accept myself as I am."
"I think there is another way."
"I love and accept myself as I am."

2. Top of your head
"Thank you, [fear/ anger/ sadness/ ...]."
"Thank you for protecting me."

3. Inside of your eyebrows
"Thank you [fear/ anger/ sadness/ ...] for being with me for so long."

4. Side of your eyes
"Thank you [fear/ anger/ sadness/ ...] for giving me so much strength."

5. Under the eyes
"Thank you to all the negative emotions for being there, because you show me that there is always love on the other side."

6. Under your nose
"This is actually quite helpful because, without you, I wouldn't be able to see love at all."

7. Under your mouth above the chin
"Thank you."
"Thank you [fear/ anger/ sadness/ ...]."
"I thank myself for opening up in doing things differently."

8. Under your collarbone
"Maybe without the [fear/ anger/ sadness/ ...] I am not only safe but even happy."

9. Under your arm
"Maybe I am not only happy, but I can also make other people happy."

Take another deep inhale through your nose and breathe it all out through the mouth. Now rate the emotion again on a scale of 1 to 10. How intense is it for you now?

Emotion:____________ Location:_____________

Scale: 1 2 3 4 5 6 7 8 9 10

Emotion:____________ Location:_____________

Scale: 1 2 3 4 5 6 7 8 9 10

Emotion:____________ Location:_____________

Scale: 1 2 3 4 5 6 7 8 9 10

Round 4: Transform the emotion into something positive

With the garden beds tended, stones removed, and soil prepared, finally the time has come to place the seeds in the ground.

If you feel that the emotional blockages are dissolving, you can now start the fourth and positively reinforcing round. This round is about turning the former negative emotion into a positive emotion such as love, peace, or trust.... You plant affirmations in your subconscious and create a new, powerful energy in your body.
Connect with your positive emotions, say affirming sentences, and tap all 9 acupressure points again:

1. Outer edge of your hand
"Hello [love/ peace/ trust/ ...]!"
"I love you."
"I am ready for [love/ peace/ trust/ ...]!"
"I say yes to [love/ peace/ trust/ ...]!"
"I love and accept myself as I am."

2. Top of your head
"Even if I haven't managed it until now, I am making a new choice and it feels so good."
"Everything that has happened so far has been so right because that is the only way I can make this decision."

3. Inside of your eyebrows
"With such power and clarity, I choose [love/ peace/ trust/ ...]!"

4. Side of your eyes
"I know that I am always protected and loved and safe."

5. Under your eyes
"Within me is the source of everything I need."

6. Under your nose
"I go into my heart, open it, and am simply there."
"I love and accept myself as I am because this is exactly how I am right."

7. Under your mouth above the chin
"Right now, right here, I am exactly right. It feels so good!"
"Hello me, I've missed you. It's great that you're back. I'm looking forward to seeing you!"

8. Under your collarbone
"I'm looking forward to it! Finally, my life is starting. How happy I am to bring all this into the world."
"It is about time. I am done with fear/ anger/ sadness/ ..."
"I don't give a damn what other people are doing."

"I choose [love/ peace/ trust/ ....] and I'm going for it now!"
"I am [love/ peace/ trust/ ....]! I am me!"

9. Under your arm
"Thank you! Thank you! Thank you!"

Place your hands in your lap and breathe in and out deeply. Feel into yourself. Feel yourself, sense. Now rate again on a scale from 1 to 10 where you would classify your emotion and whether it is still there at all.

Emotion:____________ Location:_____________

Scale: 1 2 3 4 5 6 7 8 9 10

Emotion:____________ Location:_____________

Scale: 1 2 3 4 5 6 7 8 9 10

Emotion:____________ Location:_____________

Scale: 1 2 3 4 5 6 7 8 9 10

The 6-Point Sequence

The 6-point sequence is a simplified version but has proven to be equally effective. Here we tap fewer points and adapt our sentence as we go.

Test which suits you best. Some people are drawn to the structured 9-point sequence, while others prefer the free-flowing 6-point sequence.

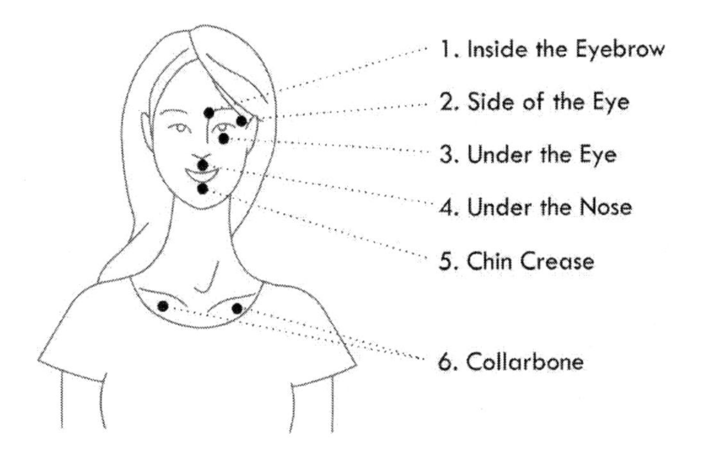

Tap points 1 to 5 about 10 to 20 times each.

When you have reached point 6, below the collarbone joint, spread the thumb and index finger of one hand about 3-4 inches (7 cm) apart and then **tap both points simultaneously**.

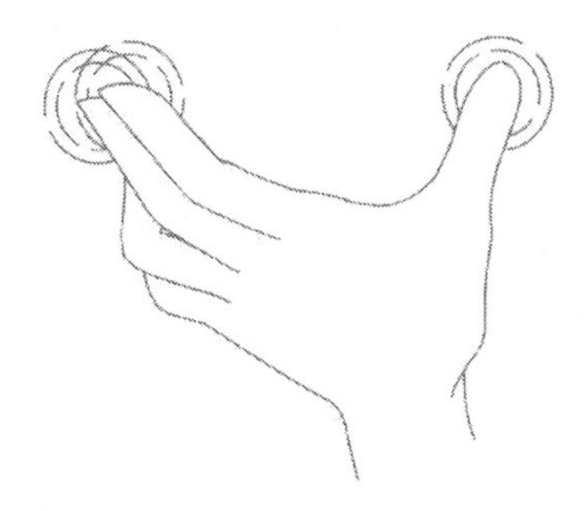

Tap on it **until the stressful feeling or negative belief has dissolved or a new emotion arises**. In this case, start with the new emotion again at point one.

Let's take insomnia as an example. Your first tapping statement could be "My fear of not being able to sleep at night".

Say this sentence several times continuously and out loud while tapping points 1-6.

Ask yourself at the end of the sequence: “What do I feel now?”. The fear of not being able to sleep may have changed to anger or sadness, for example. Then tap your anger or sadness next.

The sentence is continuously adapted to the emotion you feel at the moment. For example, “my fear of not being able to sleep at night” can become “my anger at not being able to sleep at night” and then “my worry at not being able to perform at work tomorrow”.

Try out points 1-5. Here you only need to repeat the sentence once and tap about 10 times before you move to the next tapping point.

Once you reach point 6, keep tapping while repeating the sentence until the negative emotion disintegrates. To help you, you can also classify the feelings on a scale of 0-10 and keep tapping until the value is 0.

The important thing with *Meridian Tapping* is to know you cannot do anything wrong and to always stay in the present. Concentrate on the emotion in the foreground now.

This way, you dissolve the different layers of your stressful emotional world one after the other. You can imagine the principle like peeling an onion. When all the stressful emotions have been dissolved, you should feel neutral or even peaceful and calm.

Frequently Asked Questions

During your first tapping experience, it is normal to come up with questions. Below, you will find the most frequently asked Questions and their Answers:

Is the tapping order important?

There is no specific order needed for it to work, as long as all the points are tapped in sequence.

Traditionally tapping starts with the hand and ends with the side of your ribs, but you might also start tapping from top to bottom, if you prefer.

Which (body) side should I tap?

You can tap either side.

My hand gets tired, can I switch?

Yes, you can switch the hands and sides you tap.

Why would I want to voice my negative emotions? Won't I simply attract more of it?

On the contrary, by identifying these unpleasant thoughts, emotions, experiences, beliefs, and symptoms aloud while tapping, you ensure that your focus lies on the energetic blockage. It also makes it easier for you to recognize whether the emotion is actually still there or whether it already dissolved.

Denying the existence of negative emotions, just thinking happy thoughts doesn't make them go away.

Can I tap an emotion linked to a past event?

We only tap if the negative emotions are still present.

This means you either tap right in the event when unpleasant emotions arise or if the negative emotions still are present when thinking about a past event.

How can I use tapping as a morning routine if I don't feel a negative emotion for the day ahead?

If you have no uncomfortable situations to worry about, you can practice by setting the tone of the day with positive affirmations.

Is it normal to feel thirsty after tapping?

Yes, this is completely normal. The negative feelings are detoxified and eliminated on a physical level. You should support this natural process by drinking two liters of still water a day, preferably starting already before the tapping sequence.

Is it normal to have other physical sensations during tapping?

Keep tapping when physical sensations like yawning, digestive nausea, burping, or sleepiness appear. Also fear or other emotions may arise, these are valid points that need attention. Note them down and tap them.

What if it doesn't work?

Start tapping exactly that! Create tapping statements with your questions, thoughts, and emotions until you feel neutral about the topic again. Do you feel disappointed, annoyed or angry about it?

"This isn't working for me."
"I am not having any results."
"My frustration that I am not getting anywhere."
"I knew it was too easy to be true. "

CHAPTER 4

When Should I Tap?

Daily circumstances

Make tapping a regular part of your day! You can do it in the morning to set a positive affirmation for the day, to eliminate annoyances during breaks at work, or before bedtime to release any accumulated stress.

Tapping can also be immediately implemented to help manage stressful situations and promote a more positive mindset.

Make it a habit, whether you are on the bus, in the supermarket, or at the office. Tapping just the collarbone point when in public might be a good alternative to feeling more comfortable. Visiting changing cabins or a public toilet can give you even more privacy if needed.

Finally, let's chart out how to tackle this:

1. Start paying attention to your emotions.
2. Practice identifying what emotion might be linked to any discomfort.
3. Use *Meridian Tapping* daily—even when not facing any specific ailment—to set positive affirmations and maintain overall balance.

Daily circumstances can range from everything that hinders you in the flow of your daily routine; from *cravings* to *sleep disorders* or *phobias*.

If you suffer from severe trauma, it's advisable to consult with a TFT, EFT or MET professional to determine the underlying cause and appropriate course of action.

Negative Emotions

Negative emotions are feelings that are generally unpleasant or uncomfortable, such as anger, fear or grief. They can vary in intensity and duration, and individuals may experience them in response to different situations or stimuli. It's important to note that while these emotions are generally considered negative, they are natural and provide valuable information about our needs, help navigate social situations, and promote personal growth and resilience. However, excessive or prolonged negative emotions can have adverse effects on mental and physical well-being. Tapping these specific emotions and situations will help you release blockages, and restore balance.

Unconscious Beliefs & Convictions

In addition to negative emotions, negative beliefs, and convictions are also a powerful force that promotes the development of physical symptoms. If such beliefs are valid for you, they should be resolved through tapping.

These days, many of our issues are rooted in negative beliefs and convictions about money and self-esteem, such as *"No reward without hard work."* or *"I am not good enough."*

Physical Symptoms: The Onion Peel Principle

The joys of being human! Physical symptoms are observable and measurable bodily changes or sensations that may accompany various emotions, medical conditions, or psychological states. These symptoms can manifest in response to stress, emotional experiences, or underlying health issues. This is why it is so important to get to the root of our emotions and tap them when they arise before we even get this far.

Note that physical symptoms alone may not be definitive indicators of a specific condition, as they can overlap and have various potential causes.

If you are experiencing persistent or severe physical symptoms consult with a healthcare professional to determine the underlying cause and appropriate course of action.

Be gentle and patient with yourself. Start with smaller issues like an oncoming cold or headache. The small victories will instill trust in tapping and yourself.

Positive Affirmations

Positive Affirmations can be used to set the tone of the day or during a taping sequence. Once the intensity of the negative thought, emotion, experience, belief, or symptom decreases while taping, shift to positive affirmations. Replace the negative statements with empowering and positive statements. Continue tapping your preferred Meridian Tapping Sequence while repeating these positive affirmations.

CHAPTER 5

Situations from A to Z

This chapter gives you an overview of the most common issues that are addressed with *Meridian Tapping*.

Some of these situations and statements will resonate with you, ready for you to start tapping, while others won't.

But more importantly, this overview of situations & statements serves as a template and gives you an understanding of how to address the issue and adapt or create your personal tapping statements.

Original statement:
"My frustration that I have a [headache] again."

Adapted statements:
"My frustration that I have a toothache again."
"My frustration that I have a swollen joint again."
"My anger that I have an earache again."

You pick and adapt until it matches exactly your situation and emotion.

Step 1: Identify the issue

Step 2: Rate the issue

Step 3: Choose the tapping sequence

Step 4: Set up statements

Step 5: Tap and reevaluate

Allergies

Negative Emotions & Physical Symptoms

People who develop allergies are on the increase, especially children. Their immune system reacts to foreign bodies such as certain foods, animal hair, pollen, grass, metals, house dust, and much more. Most of these things are completely harmless and do not trigger any reaction in others.

Regardless of what a person is allergic to, their quality of life is increasingly restricted. The curious thing is that those affected often develop an allergy to things that they actually like. This is particularly noticeable in the case of animal hair, and food intolerances. Even people who love dogs, cats, or horses more than anything else, and who like to eat certain foods such as strawberries, apples, citrus fruits, and dairy products, can develop an allergy to them. The person affected has no choice but to avoid contact with the allergen.

It is important that you tap into the feelings and beliefs associated with the allergy as well as the respective body symptoms.

Possible tapping sentences:

Emotions
"My sadness/my anger because I have this allergy."

"My sadness/my anger because I can no longer eat everything."
"My sadness/my anger because I can't have a pet."
"My sadness/my anger because I can no longer ride a horse."
"My sadness/my anger that my life is so restricted."
"My sadness/my anger at my body because it reacts like this."
"My sadness/my anger at myself for reacting so sensitively."
"My fear of coming into contact with the allergen."
"My fear that it won't go away."
"My fear that it will get worse."
"My fear that my quality of life will be increasingly restricted."
"My shame that I am so weak."
"I have resigned myself to this."
"My feeling of hopelessness that this will ever get better."

Beliefs
"There's nothing you can do anyway."
"It runs in our family, I inherited it."
"My father/mother had it too."
"I just have to live with it."
"Allergies are just part of life."

Physical symptoms
"This disgusting/ annoying/... burning sensation."

"This infuriating itching."
"This annoying runny nose."
"These watery eyes."

Allergies often can be caused by an unpleasant event or experience from the past, like the death of a pet for example. It is therefore important that you ask yourself when your allergy started. When you come across such an event or experience, tap on the feelings associated with it until they are truly resolved.

Alternative tapping sentences:

"My fear/my anger that I always had to eat what I didn't like."
"My fear/my anger that I always had to finish the food on my plate."
"My sadness/my anger that my cat/dog died back then."
"My sadness/my anger that I couldn't do anything to help my pet."
"My anger at ... that he/she did …."

Keep tapping the appropriate sentences in all cases until the feeling is resolved and you feel better. After tapping, however, carefully come into contact with the allergen again.

Anger/ Frustration

Negative Emotions

Are you feeling overwhelmed by anger and frustration? Do you find it difficult to control these intense emotions? Tap into the power of *Meridian Tapping* to release your anger and find a sense of calmness.

Possible tapping sentences:

"Even though I feel angry and frustrated, I deeply and completely accept myself."

"I release this anger that no longer serves me."

"I let go of all the frustration weighing me down."

"My anger does not define me, and I choose to release it now."

"I am open to finding healthier ways to express my emotions."

"I release the tension and anger in my body."

"I forgive myself for any past mistakes that caused frustration."

"I release any resentment I hold towards others."

"I choose peace and understanding over anger and frustration."

"I release the need to control every situation."

Burn Out

Negative Emotions & Physical Symptoms

The name says it all: you are burnt out. You have exhausted yourself. You have gone beyond your limits, which comes at a price. The causes of burnout often stem from fear, such as the fear of not being able to cope with the workload. The fear of saying no. The fear of failing. The fear of making mistakes. The fear of not being enough.

In addition to seeking medical or therapeutic help, you can recharge your batteries with *Meridian Tapping* as a precautionary measure, for example by resolving your fears.

Possible tapping sentences:

Emotions

"My fear of saying no."
"My fear of not being able to do the job."
"My fear of looking weak when asking for help."
"My fear of the huge responsibility I have to bear."
"This huge pressure of responsibility."
"My fear of not being able to fulfill the requirements."

"Everything is pointless."
"My doubts about myself and my achievements."

"I'm simply not enough."
"I always have to do more than the others."
"I am/feel responsible for everything."
"My inner turmoil."

Alternative tapping phrases after the onset of burnout:

"I can't take any more."
"I'm so exhausted."
"I am completely desperate."
"My sadness/anger that I'm so exhausted."
"My sadness of my disability to perform."
"My fear that I'll never be the same again."
"My fear that this will never go away."
"My fear that I have to live with it."
"My fear of being overwhelmed."

The background to burnout can be an unfulfilled desire for recognition or a childhood experience that you were only loved when you performed, in which case you can tap and adapt the following sentences:

Emotions
"My sadness that I was never allowed to be a child."
"My sadness that I had so much responsibility as a child."
"My grief that I was alone so much."
"My sadness that my needs were never important."

"My anger at my parents for bringing me up the way they did."
"My anger at my parents for never being there for me."
"My anger at my parents for always leaving me alone."
"Mum/Dad should finally see how much I'm suffering!"

Beliefs
"I am only loved when I achieve something."
"I am only valued when I am working hard."
"I have to do everything on my own."
"I always have to do more than the others."
"The others are more important than me."
"I have no right to be happy."
"I have no right to think about myself."
"My needs are not important."
"I only get attention when I'm suffering."

Cold/Flu

Daily Circumstances, Physical Symptoms

A cold is on the horizon. You have a slight tingling sensation in your throat and/or nose, a headache sets in, and you may also feel a little faint. None of this is too bad, but it is enough to get your attention. Now is the right time to stop the cold from progressing by tapping.

Firstly, please make sure that you really want to get well, or whether deep down inside you have a tiny desire to be ill again, to suffer, to lie in bed and be nursed. This could well stand in the way of your recovery. So, if you do have such feelings, tap the following sentences (if they apply to you) or find your formulations:

"I would like to have a proper cold again."

The usually unconscious ulterior motive behind this is that I will be cared for, pitied, comforted, and be the center of attention.

"I really want to cough again!"

Do you want to cough at someone?

Tap out these or similar sentences that correspond to your thinking until the sentence has lost its meaning.

Then you can start tapping on the approaching cold.

Possible tapping sentences:

Emotions
"My fear of catching a cold (again)."
"My fear of not being able to work."

Especially applies to the self-employed.

"My fear that the symptoms will get worse."
"My fear that my boss will be angry with me."
"My fear that I won't be able to go to work."
"My fear that I will lose my job, if I'm ill (again)."
"My anger/guilt at myself for not taking better care of myself."
"My anger at myself for being so sensitive to draughts/wet hair/cold feet."
"My guilt towards my colleagues/the team when I'm ill."

Beliefs
"I am so sensitive to draughts."
"I am so sensitive to wet hair."
"I am so sensitive to cold feet."
"My belief that I will catch it from others."
"My belief that I will get sick from wetness/ draughts/cold weather."

"My fear/belief/conviction that I will get sick/get a headache/ catch a cold from the wet/draught/cold weather."

Physical symptoms

"My scratchy throat."
"My tickling nose."
"I'm so dull, tired, and weak."

If we start tapping in good time, the cold won't break out.
If the cold has already broken out, you can simply tap the points one after the other for about ten to fifteen minutes, without tapping sentences. Or you can tap on the symptoms and the feelings associated with them:

Alternative tapping sentences:

Emotions

"My anger that I can't breathe properly."
"My despair because I'm sick again."
"My fear of suffocating because I can't get enough air."
"My fear that it will get much worse."
"My fear that it will never get well again."

Physical symptoms

"This terrible/annoying/tiring cough."

"This annoying cold."
"My blocked/dripping nose."
"My heavy limbs."
"I feel so miserable."

Keep tapping the appropriate phrases in all cases until the symptoms subside and you feel better.

Electromagnetic Hypersensitivity (EHS)

Negative Emotions, Beliefs & Convictions, Physical symptoms

The increasing exposure to radiation in everyday life can people out of balance, both physically and mentally. The sensitivity to radio waves, 5G and similar electromagnetic fields is often referred to as electromagnetic hypersensitivity (EHS). People with EHS report various symptoms that can probably be attributed to exposure to electromagnetic fields. If you cannot remedy the problem and feel helpless, tapping, an acute situation or the associated negative emotions, could be a solution.

Possible tapping sentences:

Emotions

"My [anger/frustration/...] that I am so sensitive to electromagnetic fields."
"My fear of physical discomfort."
"My fear of being mentally affected'.
"I hate [5G/electromagnetic fields/electronic devices]."
"I hate having no control over it."

Beliefs

"I am so sensitive to electromagnetic fields."
"I am helplessly at their mercy."
"I get this sensitivity from my family."
"Nobody can empathise with my situation."
"I can't stand these telephone masts!"
"This uncertainty is getting me down!"

Physical symptoms

"My tiredness."
"I'm completely exhausted."
"My cloudy head."
"My malaise."

Fear

Daily Circumstances, Negative Emotions

You will realize that tapping on your negative emotional state leads to inner peace and serenity, giving you the certainty that there is a solution for everything. You are back in your power. And from this strength, you can overcome anything.

Let's take the example of a piece of bad news.

Possible tapping sentences:
"My shock at this news."
"I just can't believe it."
"I can't believe it!"
"I don't want to believe it."
"It can't be true."
"My sadness at this news."
"My shock at this news."
"My anger that this has happened."
"My fear of what the consequences will be."
"My despair/anger/fear about the accident/the cancellation/illness..."

Grief/ Loss

Negative Emotions

Without Yin, there is no Yang. Fortunately, we humans are masters at putting difficult events behind us or at least suppressing them so that we can function again in everyday life. However, this does not mean that these emotions have been processed. Tapping offers us a way of relieving or even eliminating the worst emotional pressures such as sadness, anger, or disappointment in extreme situations.

Possible tapping sentences:

Phase 1
"My shock at the death of XY"
"I can't believe it!"
"It's probably just a bad dream."

Phase 2
"My fear of being alone."
"My grief to go on living without XY."
"My realization that I will never see XY again."
"My fear that I will forget XY if I resolve my grief."
"My feelings of guilt when I resolve my grief."
"My sadness about the transience of life."
"My sadness that I never told XY how much I love him/her."

"My sadness that I will never be able to touch/see XY again."
"Life no longer has any meaning for me."
"My helplessness."
"My self-pity."
"My anger that XY left me alone."
"My anger/rage at the doctors/nursing staff for letting this happen."
"My guilt because I wasn't there when XY died."
"I miss you so much."

The following thoughts represent possible obstacles on the way to a healthy detachment process and should be tapped:

"I am not allowed to dissolve my grief."
"I have to mourn XY, I owe it to him/her."
"I have to grieve for XY, otherwise I'll forget him/her."

Guilt / Shame/ Unworthiness

Negative Emotions, Positive Affirmations

Feelings of shame, guilt, and unworthiness are among the lowest energies you can sustain as a human being. Releasing them will have obvious benefits on your day-to-day energy, healing responses, and the universal abundance showing up in your life.

Possible tapping sentences:

Defining the negative emotion and allowing it to be there

"Even though I feel [ashamed/sorry/guilty/unworthy..], this [name issue] doesn't represent everything about me because I deeply and completely accept myself."

"Even though I feel [ashamed/sorry/guilty/unworthy..] about this [name issue], and I DON'T forgive myself for this [problem], I still deeply and completely accept myself."

"Even though I feel [ashamed/sorry/guilty/unworthy..] about this [name issue], I would never pin this on anyone else."

"Even though I feel [ashamed/sorry/guilty/ unworthy…] about this [name issue], self-blame is no better than blaming someone else.

Neutralizing the emotion

"Even though I feel [ashamed/sorry/guilty/ unworthy] about this [name issue], I deeply and completely accept myself."

"Not even one thimble-full of my [shame/guilt/ sorrow/unworthiness..] will change what happened, but somehow I still seem to feel [ashamed/sorry/guilty/unworthy…]."

"Somehow I believe that my feeling bad is helping in some way."

"Which does seem ridiculous."

Transforming the emotion into something positive

"Even though I feel [ashamed/sorry/guilty/ unworthy..] about this [name issue], I deeply and completely accept myself."

"Even though I feel [ashamed/sorry/guilty/ unworthy..] about this [name issue], I was born deserving, I'll die deserving. The only question is if I'll give myself a break for the bit in the middle."

Gnashing of Teeth

Negative Emotions, Physical Symptoms

Negative habits like teeth gnashing and nail-chewing often stem from various psychological and emotional factors and exert enormous stress on the jaw joints and teeth. To relax your jaw, you can tap the teeth-grinding issue directly along with your stress factors.

Possible tapping sentences:

"My teeth grinding at night."
"I'm embarrassed by my teeth grinding at night."
"My despair that I can't stop doing this."
"My anger about the subsequent complaints such as headaches, neck and muscle pain."
"My fear that it has already caused me permanent damage."

You can adapt the tapping statements to all bad habits:

"My stupid nail biting."

"My anger at myself because my fingers look so ugly."

Headaches/ Migraine

Negative Emotions & Physical Symptoms

Headaches are almost part of everyday life in our stress-ridden lives. They are often an expression of too much. Too much emotional pressure, too much work and general overwhelm. It would often be enough to treat yourself to a little rest, relaxation or sleep. But that's not always possible straight away. Before you reach for a pill, why not try tapping?

Possible tapping sentences:

Emotions

"My headache is driving me crazy!"
"My anger/my rage at my headache."
"My frustration that I have a headache again."
"My fear that the headache will get worse."
"My fear that it will develop into a migraine."
"My resignation that I have to live with it."
"I can't stand it!"
"My sadness that I'm in so much pain again."

Physical symptoms

"My headaches."
"My stupid headache."
"My throbbing head."
"My impaired vision."
"It hurts so much!"

Keep tapping and using the appropriate phrases in all cases until the symptoms subside and you feel better.

If your headaches are chronic, please consult a doctor to find out whether they may have an organic cause. Sometimes defective teeth can be the cause of headaches. Please ask your dentist to clarify this.

Indigestion

Negative Emotions & Physical Symptoms

Upset stomach, nausea, bad digestion, too much has been eaten or drunk. As the physical symptoms and emotions are closely linked in such complaints, in many cases it is sufficient to tap into the physical symptoms. The sentences depend entirely on your condition and are spoken in a tone that corresponds to your state of mind. If you feel like moaning, the voice will have a "miserable" coloring. If you feel disgust, this is also expressed in your voice, sometimes only in a groan or other sounds.

Possible tapping sentences:

Emotions

"My nausea."
"I feel sick."
"I feel like throwing up."
"I could throw up."
"I feel so miserable."
"I feel so disgusting."
"My fear of dying."

In all cases, keep tapping the appropriate sentences until the symptoms subside and you feel better.

If the nausea is too strong, your stomach will try to empty itself. Even if you don't feel like it, you should support this impulse. After all, it is one of our body's marvelous self-help mechanisms. However, you should tap yourself. Points 6 (collarbone points) are sufficient.

If you feel disgusted about throwing up, tap:

"My disgust at throwing up."
"This is so disgusting."

Or simply:
"Yuck, yuck, yuck!"

In this way, you make it easier for your stomach to digest the intolerable again.

Menopause

Negative emotions, physical symptoms, positive affirmations

The menopause is not an illness, but a normal phase of life. As with every new stage of life, there can be new challenges, but also new opportunities. During the menopause hormonal changes occur in the female body. They can be accompanied by various physical signs until the organism gradually adapts to the new situation. These signs can be tapped.
Changes in the menstrual cycle can also have other causes. They should therefore be examined by a doctor as a precaution. If bleeding recurs after the menopause, this is always a reason to consult a doctor.

Possible tapping sentences:

Emotions
"My frustration at losing control over my body."
"My helplessness in the face of sudden mood swings."
"My frustration of [blushing/ sweating...]."
"My sudden [nervousness/ upset/ listlessness...]".
"These constant changes of emotions."

Physical symptoms

"My irregular periods".
"This [unpleasant night sweat/ restless sleep...]".
"This sudden [racing heart/ shivering...]."
"My annoyance at never knowing how to dress myself."
"My fear of the next hot flush."

Positive affirmations

'I allow myself my physical reactions.'
'I hardly notice the [hot flushes, palpitations, shivering...]
'I sleep deeply and wake up feeling rested.'
'I feel centered.'

Money

Beliefs & Convictions, Positive Affirmations

Beliefs control our lives. Usually without us realizing it.
No area is more burdened with negative belief patterns than the topic of money. Let's be honest, abundance helps reduce stress in our everyday lives and this is why the topic of money found its way into this book about well-being. Following you will find a selection of common beliefs & convictions about money.
First, tick the sentences that resonate with you and maybe you want to write down some of your own.
Then tap the ticked sentences.
And lastly, formulate and replace them with positive ones.

Example:
Negative Belief:
"I'm too old to get rich."

Positive Belief:

"It is never too late to get rich."

- I am not intelligent enough to get rich.
- The pursuit of wealth is often at the expense of something.

- It is better to be poor and healthy than rich and sick.
- Money does not grow on trees
- I do not have sufficient education to become rich.
- Most of the good opportunities are already already passed.
- Rich people have only a few true friends.
- You can't learn to get rich.
- Getting rich as a woman is more difficult.
- You can't get rich doing what you like best.
- To get rich you have to exploit others.
- Women/Men only love me for my money.
- Money is the root of all evil.
- Money destroys character.
- A lot of money would change me so much that my partner would no longer love me.
- I always spend more money than I have.
- It's not right to earn much more money than my parents.
- Money is dirty.
- ______________________________
- ______________________________
- ______________________________

Performance

Negative Emotions, Beliefs & Convictions

If you do competitive sport, you know best how hard you train and that you are doing everything you can to get better.
Nevertheless, there may be occasional performance blocks, which often have to do with fears, doubts, or experienced failure. These need to be resolved.

Possible tapping sentences:

Emotions

"My fear of failure."
"My fear of not having trained enough."
"My fear that others are better."
"My fear of the opponent."
"My fear of risking my health."
"My concern about my last injury."
"My fear of being criticized by others."
"My fear of not being able to maintain my level."
"My frustration with my last performance."
"My fear of my coach's high expectations."

Beliefs

"I must never lose."
"I'll never be as good as XY."
"I'll never make it to the top."
"I'll always be second choice."
"I'm just not good enough."

Phobias

Daily Circumstances, Neg. Emotions, Beliefs & Convictions

Phobias are intense and irrational fears that interfere with daily life and may lead to avoidance behavior, impacting a person's ability to function in certain situations.

Phobias are a type of anxiety disorder and are classified into three main categories:

1. **Specific Phobias:** These involve a fear of a particular object, situation, or activity. Common examples include fear of spiders (Arachnophobia) or needles (Trypanophobia).
2. **Social Phobia (Social Anxiety Disorder):** This is characterized by an intense fear of social situations and the fear of being judged or embarrassed in public. It may lead to avoidance of social interactions. One of them is fear of blushing (Erythrophobia).
3. **Agoraphobia:** This involves a fear of being in situations where escape might be difficult or embarrassing or where help might not be available in the event of a panic attack. It often leads to avoiding crowded places or situations perceived as unsafe, one of them being the fear of flying (Aviophobia).

Erythrophobia

Possible tapping sentences:

"My fear of blushing."

"My fear of being hurt."

"My fear of being exposed."

"My fear of being laughed at."

"My fear that my blushing will be misinterpreted."

"My worry that I might blush at any moment."

"My anger that the possibility of blushing makes me insecure."

"My anger that the possibility of blushing restricts my actions."

"My grief that I avoid brightly lit rooms and social gatherings because I am afraid of blushing."

"My annoyance that the thought of blushing makes me blush."

"My fear of not living up to the expectations of others."

You can customize the above phobia-tapping statements to your specific phobia:

"My horror of spiders."

"My fear of being paralyzed."

"My embarrassment about the disproportionate fear of needles."

"My fear of pain."

"My anger at myself for not being able to visit my grandchildren overseas."
"My fear of dying."

Pregnancy & Birth

Negative Emotions, Positive Affirmations, Beliefs & Convictions, Physical Symptoms

One of the most beautiful experiences we can have is when a child is announcing itself. While pregnancy used to be celebrated, nowadays it is often associated with fear of the responsibility, the financial burden, and the birth itself.

Realize that pregnancy and birth are absolutely natural processes and that your body's wisdom will tell you exactly what to do.

Nowadays we also know that the thoughts and feelings that the mother has during pregnancy are absorbed unfiltered by the child. It is important to conceive a child in an atmosphere of love, joy, and trust. That is why we tap our emotions around the pregnancy, the birth and the time with the newborn.

Pregnancy (Women)

Emotions

"My fear of being pregnant."
"My fear of physical changes."
"My fear of pain during childbirth."
"My fear that I will no longer be able to work."
"My anger that I got pregnant."

Physical Symptoms

"My morning sickness."

"My dizziness."
"My ravenous appetite."

Pregnancy (Women & Men)

Emotions

"My fear of the new situation."
"My fear of not being able to cope with the stress."
"My fear that we/I won't be able to cope financially."
"My fear that our marriage will suffer if we have a child."
"My fear that our sex life will suffer if we have a child."
"My fear of having sex during pregnancy."
"My anger because I won't be able to continue my life as usual."

Pregnancy (Men)

Emotions

"My jealousy of the unborn child."
"My fear that there is now a child between us."
"My fear of not being a good father."
"My fear of responsibility."

Affirmations

"I choose to look forward to the child from now on."
"I choose to welcome the unborn child with immediate effect."

"I choose to see the child as an (unexpected) enrichment of my/our life."

Birth (Women)

Emotions

"My fear of childbirth."
"My fear of possible complications."
"My fear of pain."
"My fear of not making it to the hospital in time."
"My fear of not knowing what to expect."

Beliefs

"Every birth is painful."
"Births are dangerous."
"Every birth is a risk."

Birth (Men)

Emotions

"My fear of what's to come."
"I can't see blood."
"My fear of seeing my wife suffer."
"My fear that something will happen to my wife."

After Birth

Emotions

"I'm so exhausted."
"My horror at the sagging abdominal wall."
"My fear that my body won't return to normal."
"My fear of doing something wrong."

"My annoyance that it screams so much."
"My doubts as to whether it was the right decision."

Relationships

Negative Emotions, Beliefs & Convictions

Whether before, during, or after a partnership, this area of life is accompanied by a lot of emotions. Here you will find some suggestions of tapping sets on various topics, which you can expand as you wish.

Overcoming past relationships

Emotions

"My sadness that XY has left me."
"My sadness that we didn't make it."
"My anger that I failed (again)."
"My anger that XY broke up with me."
"My fear of being alone."

Entering into a new relationship

Emotions

"My fear of entering into a new partnership."
"My fear of losing my independence."
"My fear of being left again."
"My fear of not being attractive enough."

Beliefs

"Nobody wants me anyway."
"I don't deserve a happy partnership."
"I don't need a partner."
"I only get hurt anyway."

Communication

Emotions

"My fear of sharing my thoughts with my partner."
"My fear that our marriage will end like my parents'"
"My resignation because we talk to each other so little."
"My fear of being rejected for who I am."

Self-Love

Negative Emotions, Positive Affirmations

The rejection of one's own body. Many people have a strained relationship with their own body. We don't like it, hate it as a whole or parts of it. Only when we have a loving relationship with our body will we feel comfortable in it. This is the prerequisite for self-acceptance, inner balance, and a natural relationship with our sexuality. Tapping supports you in this process.

Possible tapping sentences:

Emotions

"I hate my body!"
"I'm ashamed of my body."
"I'm disgusted by my body."
"I hate my body because of its shape."
"I hate my body because it's so fat/skinny."
"I hate my body because it is always sick."
"I think my bum is shapeless."
"I don't like my breasts because they are too small/large."
"I'm ashamed of my wide hips."
"I hate my pot belly."
"I'm ashamed because I'm so small/tall."
"I'm ashamed of my cellulite."
"I am ashamed of my genitals."

Positive Affirmations

"From now on, I choose to accept my body as it is."

"I allow myself to love my body from now on."

"I choose to enjoy my body."

"I am grateful for my body."

Sexuality

Negative Emotions, Positive Affirmations

If you can enjoy your body and sexuality, you can skip this chapter. However, if you feel fear and shame towards your sex, tapping is necessary. If you have had negative sexual experiences or traumatic events, you may want to seek therapeutic support.

Possible tapping sentences:

Emotions (mostly women)

"My fear of sex."
"My fear of losing control over myself."
"My feelings of guilt when I enjoy sex."

Beliefs

"Sex is a sin."
"Sex is dirty."
"Sex is not important."
"Sex should not be fun."

Emotions (mostly men)

"My frustration because I'm not having enough sex."
"My frustration when my body doesn't perform the way I want it to."
"My fear of not getting it up."
"My fear of coming too early."

Sleep Disorders

Negative Emotions, Positive Affirmation

Sufficient, healthy sleep duration is a vital part of our physical and mental well-being. Yet 30% - 40% of American adults complain of insomnia symptoms. The causes are usually worry, fear, grief, stress, or emotional strain.
Check exactly what is depriving you of sleep and tap into these emotional issues.

Possible tapping sentences:

Emotions

"I can't fall asleep."
"My frustration because I can't fall asleep."
"My fear that I won't be able to sleep again tonight."
"My fear of waking up and not being able to fall asleep again."
"My fear of not being able to perform well the next day.

Positive Affirmations

"I choose to sleep peacefully from now on."
"I sleep deeply and wake up well rested."
"I choose to sleep through the night from now on."
"I allow myself to sleep through the night from now on."

Sprains

Physical Symptoms, Negative Emotions

Sprains, dislocations, and bruises can happen so quickly. you can use tapping to quickly relieve the symptoms. When you start tapping, you will probably not be able to form well-formed sentences because the pain is too intense. You may even only be able to moan. Start by tapping on your pain, tapping each phrase that applies to you, and keep tapping until the pain subsides.

Possible tapping sentences:

Physical symptoms

"Ouch, ouch, that hurts!"
"I'm in so much pain."
"I'm about to faint."
"I can't stand this."

Emotions; tap alternating with the pain

"It sucks that this happened to me!"
"My anger/my anger at myself."
"I am an f*** idiot for not paying attention."
"If only I had paid more attention."
"What a bummer, now I can't take care on my children/go on holiday/do any more sport."
"Shit, now I've got a cast/bandage and can only walk with crutches."

"My anger/my frustration that I am now out of action for a long time."
"My frustration that I am in so much pain."
"My anger that I have caused myself such pain."
"Why does something like this always have to happen to me?"
"I feel so sorry for myself because I fell."

Keep tapping in the appropriate sentences in all cases until the symptoms subside and you feel better.
In the case of minor injuries, improvement can occur very quickly. For severe dislocations in conjunction with bruises and sprains, you will need to tap over a longer period, on a daily basis. Of course, the injured body part must be kept still and cooled. In the case of serious injuries, always consult with a medical professional or go to the hospital.

Stage Fright

Negative Emotions, Positive Affirmations, Beliefs & Convictions, Physical Symptoms

For very few people it is a joyful moment to have to give a speech, whether privately at a family celebration or professionally as a speaker, at a presentation, job interview, or as an actor and musician. Fear and excitement usually cloud the event. Physical symptoms such as restlessness, sweating, trembling, or diarrhea set in.
If a previous experience still harbors negative emotions, these should be tapped first.

Possible tapping sentences:

"My anger at myself for failing back then."
"My fear that it will happen to me again."
"My disappointment because I messed up."

Before the next event:
"My stage fright."
"My nervousness."
"I am so excited."
"It's all too much."
"I can't handle it."
"My fear that my voice will fail."
"My fear that the others can see my excitement."
"My fear of not making it."

"It's bound to go wrong."
"My fear of not remembering my speech."
"My fear that my hands are shaking"
"My fear that you can see that I'm sweating"
"My fear of blushing"
"I can hardly breathe with excitement."
"My anger at myself that I can't just be calm."
"My envy of the others because they are better."

Once your negative feelings have dissipated and you are relaxed when you think about your performance, you can reinforce this feeling of well-being with positive affirmations:

"With such power and clarity, I choose to be calm and composed during my speech."
"...I choose to remember the text freely and speak fluently."
"...I choose to enjoy being the center of attention."

Technical Devices

Beliefs & Convictions

Technical innovations and changes are coming at us at a breathtaking pace; hardly a day goes by without some innovation in the technology market demanding our attention. For some people, this is pure bliss while for others it is pure horror. In the professional world particularly, this can lead to stress. Internal resistance makes working with the new technologies even more difficult. Sentences like "I used to be able to do the same work without a computer." are often heard when dealing with stress and excessive demands in a digital workplace. And it is no coincidence that we are already talking about "technostress" which is also based on fears.

With the help of *Meridian Tapping*, you can develop a relaxed relationship with technology and learn to use it to your advantage.

Possible tapping sentences:

Emotions

"My fear of technical devices."
"My fear of not being able to understand."
"My fear of being overwhelmed."
"My fear of not being able to keep up."
"My fear of the internet."
"My fear of being tracked down."
"My fear of overloading my computer."

"My fear of never learning."
"My fear of pressing the wrong button and deleting something."
"My fear of the many technical innovations of our time."
"My fear that computer work will damage my eyes."

But perhaps you also feel defiance and resistance alongside your fear?

"My defiance/resistance to computers/technology."
"I refuse to deal with it! "
"I don't understand the need for it at all! "
"It used to be different."
"Everything used to be nicer without all this technical stuff."

Toothache

Negative Emotions, Physical Symptoms

It's the weekend, you have an unbearable toothache and you cannot reach a dentist. You have taken a painkiller, but it doesn't help much. Tapping the pain and inflammation has worked for many people before. Try it out and see if it works for you too.

Possible tapping sentences:
"My unbearable toothache."
"My fear that it will get worse."
"I'm going crazy with pain."

Keep tapping on the sentences that are right for you until you notice the desired result. However, please go to the dentist as soon as possible so that he or she can carry out any necessary treatment.

Weather sensitivity

Physical Symptoms & Beliefs & Convictions

Weather sensitivity can really throw some people off balance - physically and mentally. If You feel helplessly at the mercy of these problems, tapping could be a solution. Why not try it out in advance, as a preventative measure (address the negative emotions linked to it), or in an acute situation.

Possible tapping sentences:

Feelings

"My anger that I am so sensitive to weather."
"My fear of circulatory collapse."
"I hate thunderstorms/high pressure/humidity."

Beliefs

"I am so sensitive to weather fluctuations. "
"I got this sensitivity from my family. "
"I'm helplessly at the mercy of it."
"There's nothing one can do."
"Approaching thunderstorm throw me off track!"
"I can't stand thunderstorms/rain/clouds etc.!"
"I'm always so depressed when it rains."

Physical symptoms

"My tiredness."
"I'm completely exhausted."
"My cloudy head."

Weight Loss

Negative Emotions, Positive Affirmations

Tapping lowers your levels of cortisol, a stress hormone. Elevated cortisol does have a relationship with weight gain and binge eating patterns. If you stabilize your cortisol level through tapping, it can support weight loss.
If you're an emotional eater, *Meridian Tapping* might help curb your appetite and lead to weight loss.

If you believe you're gaining weight because of stress, *Meridian Tapping* might help with that, too.

But if you're simply trying to lose some excess weight, there are other methods you can use in addition to tapping – paying attention to a healthy diet with fresh seasonal ingredients instead of ready-made meals in combination with regular physical activity for example.

Emotions

"I have overeaten"

"I am stuffed."

"I feel gross."

"My anger that I've overeaten again."

"My disgust that I have overeaten."

"My guilt because I ate too much."

Affirmations

"I want to take care of my body"

"I deserve to feel good in my body"

"I choose to accept my body."

"My body is perfect as it is."

"I choose to love my body."

"I choose to listen to my body."

"I choose to eat when I am hungry."

TAP TIP

The Collarbone

Point 6, the collarbone point, is the most important and can be used on its own for dissolving negative emotions. Simply tap with your thumb and index (or thumb and middle finger) about 2 cm below the collarbone on both sides simultaneously while repeating your tapping statements. Keep tapping while repeating your statement until the negative emotion disintegrates. To help you, you can also classify the feelings on a scale of 0-10 and keep tapping until the value is 0.

Summary & Conclusion

The power of *Meridian Tapping* is transformative. It's like having a personal wellness tool at your fingertips. By acknowledging our challenges, embracing self-acceptance, and fostering positive affirmations, we open the door to a more balanced and resilient state of mind. As you tap into the wisdom of your body's energy system, this practice becomes a trusted companion on your path to greater emotional freedom and self-healing. *Meridian Tapping* is more than just a technique; it's a game changer.

1. Identify the Issue: Recognize a specific issue, emotion, or thought that you'd like to address. It could be stress, anxiety, a limiting belief, a negative memory, or a physical challenge.

2. Rate the Intensity: On a scale from 0 to 10, assess the intensity of the issue. This will help you measure your progress and determine when to stop tapping on a particular concern.

3. Create a Setup Statement: Form a simple statement that acknowledges the issue and includes self-acceptance. For example: "Even though I feel stressed about [specific situation], I deeply and completely accept myself."

4. Tapping Sequence: Follow a tapping sequence of your choice. (1-Point, 6-Point or 9-Point Sequence)

5. Repeat as Needed: Go through the tapping sequence several times, focusing on reducing the intensity of the negative emotion. You can adapt the statement as you notice changes in your emotions.

6. Positive Affirmations: Once the intensity decreases, shift to positive affirmations. Replace the negative statements with empowering and positive ones. Continue tapping on the meridian points while repeating these affirmations.

7. Integrate Tapping into Your Routine: Make tapping a regular part of your day. You can do it in the morning to set a positive tone for the day, during breaks at work, or before bedtime to release any accumulated stress.

8. Adapt Tapping Statements for Various Situations: Tapping is versatile and can be used for different situations, such as public speaking, anxiety, fear of failure, relationship issues, boosting performance, or general stress. Customize your tapping statements and affirmations based on the provided tapping statements and the specific challenges you're facing.

9. Stay Consistent: Consistency is key. Practice tapping regularly to experience its cumulative benefits. As you become more comfortable with the technique, you may find it easier to apply it in various situations.

Remember that tapping is a personal practice, and what works for one person may differ for another. Experiment with tapping in different situations, and adapt the technique to suit your needs and preferences. If you find it challenging to do on your own, consider seeking guidance from a qualified TFT, EFT, or MET practitioner.

If facing severe or persistent symptoms, always consult a medical professional alongside practicing energy tapping. It's essential to approach your path to well-being holistically—considering both physical and mental well-being.

***

I hope you've enjoyed my book! I'd love to read about your first tapping experiences –no matter how small they appear; they may be encouraging to others.

In that case, if you liked my book, I would be grateful for your review directly from your Amazon account –and remember, a tap a day keeps the doctor away!

Happy Tapping!

INDEX

Made in United States
Troutdale, OR
10/25/2024

24132591R00064